Introduction

Think about it. How often do you connect to a farm? Answer: at least three times a day. Everytime we eat a meal, or have a snack, we are relying on a farm because just about everything we eat is reared or grown by farmers. Farming is the foundation of civilisation but most people know very little about where their food comes from or how it is grown.

This guidebook aims to tell you about farming in general – and organic farming in particular. Organic farmers use methods which place strong emphasis on protecting the environment. They also have to ensure that their animals can range freely outdoors and have plenty of space.

This guide book will give you a fascinating insight into what you may find on an organic farm. There are a host of things to look out for and some fun activities too. The guide is designed to be used during a visit or read in its own right. We learn how organic farms are helping to enhance wildlife and conserve our countryside. This book takes us on a journey of discovery – enjoy!

Contents

Farming

MAP STICK

Make a 'map' of your trip to an organic farm. Collect colourful and interesting things as you go round the farm to remind you of the day. Tie them to a stick with grass stems.

DID YOU KNOW?

76 per cent of land in the UK is farmland. Farmers therefore play an important role in shaping our countryside.

Agriculture

Throughout history farming has shaped the land. For instance iron age farmers changed the landscape from forest to a farmed countryside. Over the last 50 years, there has been another dramatic change. Industrial-type farming has tended to produce a single commodity (like corn) and use chemicals to feed the crop and kill pests and weeds. Such farming aims to be efficient, but growing one crop, year after year with chemicals, has had a damaging effect on the countryside.

Organic farming and organic standards

Organic farmers aim to farm with the least ecological damage, to conserve and enhance wildlife and land. Many non-organic farmers also have a similar approach – but organic farming is enforced by strict rules. These are called organic standards.

Organic standards are laid down in law. Anything labelled 'organic' must legally meet the required standard. These standards cover all aspects of food production from animal welfare and wildlife conservation, to prohibiting artificial food additives.

DID YOU KNOW?

Over the last 50 years our countryside has lost:

- 95 per cent of wildflower meadows
- 82 per cent of partridges
- 75 per cent of skylarks (60 per cent lost since 1972)
- 50 per cent of natural woodland
- 40 per cent of hedgerows.

However, research has shown that compared to non-organic farms, organic farms have:

- 44 per cent more birds in fields
- 25 per cent more birds at field margins
- More than five times as many wild plants in arable fields
- 1.6 times as many insects.

FARM DETECTIVE

Pretend you are a detective, or a Soil Association inspector, who is looking for clues about how the organic farm works. This guidebook will help you; for example, can you find:

- Some clover
- Wildlife habitats
- Something that smells nice
- Something that smells nasty
- Evidence of humans
- Mini-beasts
- Different tree species.

Soil Association standards

The Soil Association sets its own standards which tend to be higher than those set down in law. It is the oldest and most experienced organic certifier in the UK and licenses about 80 per cent of our organic food. The Soil Association is a not-for-profit organisation, respected both nationally and internationally for its integrity and pioneering role.

Conversion to organic

Farms must go through at least two years of conversion before they achieve organic status. This conversion time gives the land a clean break from chemical applications and allows the farmer to plant fertility-building clover.

A Soil Association inspector will visit a farm at least once a year to check that the standards are being followed and only then will the Soil Association organic symbol be awarded.

Look out for the Soil Association's symbol on organic food. It is your guarantee that food has been produced to the highest organic standards.

WHAT DOES IT MEAN?

Arable fields – fields cultivated to grow crops like cereals.
Field margins – edges of the field by hedges or stone walls.

A NATURAL MAP

From a good viewpoint look over the farm. Look at the type of landscape, fields, trees, rivers, and buildings. Make a picture of what you can see out of natural materials (twigs, leaves, grass and stones).

Soil

Soil is essential to life. Healthy soil has food, air and water to help plants grow. In turn animals feed on the crops and humans feed on both plants and animals. The Soil Association believes that our health depends on a healthy soil.

Most of the plant's nourishment comes from the soil. The nutrients are made up of minerals from the earth, ground down from rocks into tiny particles over time. Other nutrients come from dead plants and animals, also broken down over time by the insects and bugs which live in the soil.

COMPOST HEAP

Compost is produced from decaying vegetable matter. As it decays, the heap heats up – often to over 60°C. The heat kills off weed seeds and diseases. Try measuring the temperature of a compost heap to see how hot it is.

WHAT SOIL AM I?

. . . .

The farmer would like your help in finding out what soil is on the farm. Use the method below to help find out.

- Wet the soil sample and squeeze until no more water comes out
- Knead it for a few moments in your hand. Try to make the shapes shown on the facing page
- The shape you can make indicates the soil texture (for example, if a worm shape can be made but it breaks if bent, it is a loam).

Compare the shapes on the opposite page with the shape you've got.

Soil Life

....

A living soil is teeming with life, from earthworms, centipedes and beetles to fungi and bacteria, bugs so tiny you need a microscope to see them.

Plants cannot use most of the minerals and other essential elements in the soil directly, so they have to be converted to a useable form (humus) by these creatures. The plants in turn help these organisms by secreting sugars and enzymes back into the soil.

Soil forms slowly but can be lost rapidly through erosion. It can also be contaminated by pollution. Organic farming protects and improves soil by:

- Restricting artificial chemicals because they suppress soil life
- Adding nutrients through composted farm manure and green waste
- Establishing crop rotation because different crops put in or take out different nutrients and it is important to balance crop growing and building soil fertility
- Encouraging hedgerows, windbreaks and smaller fields to reduce wind erosion
- Planting cover crops to protect soil from wind, rain and nutrient loss.

WHAT SOIL AM I?

....

Sand
(cone shape)

Sand/loam
(ball)

Loam
(worm)

Loam/clay
(bent cracked worm)

Clay
(smooth bent worm)

NAME THAT FIELD

Find out the names of local fields and think about the reasons for these names. If you can't find them, perhaps make up your own field names which describe them (for example Oak Tree Field, above).

When you are walking the farm, look out for features that give clues to the history of the field.

Fields

For many centuries most people grew their own food – crops were farmed on open land by villagers in a communal way. This system changed during the industrial revolution when towns filled with factory workers unable to grow their own food. The need to increase food production stimulated new ways of farming, with new equipment: this led to the agricultural revolution. Landowners wanted to implement these methods – the Enclosure Acts (1750–1850) gave landowners the right to enclose common land with boundaries, changing the landscape from open land to the 'traditional' patchwork of fields.

Just as the Enclosure Acts and new ways of farming impacted on the landscape, so field patterns changed again in the last half century. Intensive farming practices have led to the removal of hedgerows and the enlargement of fields into large tracts of land.

However, organic farmers often reverse this trend, reducing field size to aid crop rotation and create habitats for beneficial predatory creatures.

WHAT DOES IT MEAN?

Crop rotation – when two or more crops are grown in a field in a sequence (for instance: clover, followed by a cereal, followed by a root crop followed by a cereal), pests and disease do not accumulate. This helps with pest control, weed control and soil fertility.

DID YOU KNOW?

Celtic field systems are some of the earliest forms of farming in the UK, dating back 5,000 years.

Ridge and furrow is an ancient farming practice which produces distinctive ridges and dips or 'furrows' across permanent pasture.

Hedgerows

HOW OLD IS THAT HEDGE?

You can estimate the age of a hedge by counting the different types of trees and shrubs in it. Take a 30 metre length section of an ancient hedge. For each different species counted the hedgerow is 100 years old. How old is the hedge that you can see?

Some hedgerows may date from ancient woodland that once covered the country. The patchwork of hedgerows was greatest in the 19th century, providing a haven for flora, fauna and wildlife. But in the last half century, industrial farming practices have led to the destruction of thousands of miles of hedgerow.

Organic farmers recognise the importance of hedges for the landscape, wildlife, and shelter for farm animals. Hedges need management to maintain them in stock-proof condition by 'laying' the hedge every few years (pictured). This work is done in the winter and, if a different hedge is layered each year, will provide a variety of habitats for wildlife on the farm.

DID YOU KNOW?

Between 1984 and 1993, the length of managed hedgerows in the UK decreased by nearly a third. Soil Association organic standards prohibit:

- The removal of hedges and banks without permission from the Soil Association
- Hedge trimming between April and August due to the damage it would do to nesting birds and flowering plants.

WHAT DOES IT MEAN?

Stock – livestock or farm animals.
Hedge 'laying' or **layering** – when partly cut stems are bent over and woven with others to renew the hedge.

Hedgerows and stone walls vary throughout the country. Look out for different boundary types:

- West country hedges tend to be planted on a bank whilst the Midland hedge grows straight out of the ground
- Dry stone walls in Snowdonia may be made from upright slabs of slate whilst Cornish stone walls have a turf top (pictured).

Stone walls

Dry stone walls are found in many parts of Britain where stone is plentiful. There are many regional variations but the same building principles apply.

Dry stone walls may appear lifeless but they provide valuable homes for plants, animals and insects in exposed areas. Many varieties of flowering plants, ferns, lichens and mosses find them an ideal habitat. The sunny face of the wall is desert-like, but the shaded side favours moisture-loving plants. Insects and small animals live in and around the walls – basking on the sunny side and living and breeding in the wall itself.

BUILD A STONE WALL

Take a few small stones and see if you can build a miniature dry stone wall. Does your wall stand up?

BARN BUILDER

....

Look at the farm buildings and think what materials have been used in their construction. Can you work out whether a building is old or new by looking at the design and materials with which it is made? What are the building materials you can see?

stone thatch slate brick wood

steel corrugated glass concrete iron

Farm buildings

....

When you visit the farm you will probably find a range of buildings, both old and new, all designed for a different purpose. Traditional farm buildings have evolved over centuries using local materials and techniques. This may be cob (a mixture of clay and straw) in Devon, timber framed in the Welsh borders or granite in Scotland.

Some buildings would be used for milking cows, others for storing grain, stabling the horses and so on. You may be able to identify what the original use and names for these buildings were. However, modern farming methods and mechanisation have made many of these building redundant and they have been replaced with large, open steel-framed buildings. Despite this, many traditional farm buildings have new uses as holiday accommodation, farm shops or offices.

Organic standards define the amount of space and housing requirements for organic livestock. This helps to ensure the highest animal welfare when animals are being housed.

DID YOU KNOW?

Over the last 50 years farms have become increasingly mechanised. The work of the horse and farm labourers have been largely replaced by tractors and machines.

A SIX YEAR ROTATION

Year 1 – cattle

Year 2 – sheep

Year 3 – wheat

(continued opposite)

Rotations

Rotations have formed the traditional base for agriculture since Roman times and were further developed during the 18th century. The most famous was the Norfolk four course rotation: clover; wheat; turnips; barley. Rotation prevents the build up of pests and disease and the depletion of nutrients. However 20th century developments in pesticides and fertilisers have led some farmers to abandon rotations in favour of monoculture and chemicals.

Organic rotations

Rotation is at the heart of organic farming. Organic farmers plant alternate groups of plants (roots, cereals, brassicas, legumes) to build up soil fertility. Some plants, like clover, add fertility to the soil – while wheat and potatoes use up nutrients.

A rotation of crops around the farm over a number years will aim to balance crops which build fertility with those that demand nutrients. So a year of potatoes is followed by a year of clover.

A SIX YEAR ROTATION

Year 4 – beans

Year 5 – oats

Year 6 – turnips

WHAT DOES IT MEAN?

Ley – when land is sown with grass then ploughed up, as part of a rotation. Leys allow the land to rest and rebuild fertility.

Monoculture – growing the same crop on the same field year after year.

Pesticides – poisonous chemicals used to kill pests. Pesticides also include herbicides (which kill weeds), fungicides and insecticides. 'Cide' comes from the Latin *caedere* meaning to kill.

Fertiliser – applied to crops to improve growth and yield. Can be artificial chemicals or natural products (for example manure).

Clover leys

Clover leys (see photograph) form the foundation of any organic farm. Clover has nodules on its roots that 'fix' nitrogen into the soil, providing the nutrition that enables crops to flourish. Sometimes you may see clover being grown under cereals. This undersowing provides a certain amount of nutrition for the current crop and a head start for that ley.

Fertility building

Organic farmers aim to recycle nutrients to keep brought-in manures to a minimum. Soil fertility normally comes from grass/clover leys, legume crops (peas and beans) and composted livestock manures. The crop rotation balances those crops which create fertility, with those which use up a lot of nutrients.

Livestock are also rotated around most organic farms to provide 'clean grazing' and to prevent the build up of parasites or diseases.

DID YOU KNOW?

Rotation fulfils the following important roles:

- Provides nutrition for crops through clover leys and composted farm manure
- Controls weeds, pests and disease problems
- Maintains the soil organic matter and structure.

Some studies estimate that only half the amount of artificial nitrogen fertilisers is actually used by plants. The rest can 'leach' into rivers and streams, causing pollution. Nitrate levels are beginning to exceed levels set by European law – so it is important to use alternatives to chemical fertilisers, such as clover.

WHAT DOES IT MEAN?

Germination – when a seed starts to grow by sprouting roots and shoots.

Mulching – when material like straw or plastic sheeting is applied to the soil surface to protect the plant.

Microclimate – climate of a small area that is different from that of the surrounding area.

DID YOU KNOW?

Organic farmers tolerate a certain amount of weed growth as long as the weeds don't affect the value of the crop. Weeds can provide:

- Valuable ground cover to protect the soil
- A microclimate
- Homes for predatory insects.

Weed and pest control

• •

Weeds are unwanted plants that can harm the crops being grown. They compete for space, light, water and nutrients and can reduce the value of the final crop.

Weed control

• •

Organic farmers do not use any herbicides and therefore rely on other methods to manage weeds. These are:

- Crop rotation
- Timely cultivations before or after sowing can stop germination of weeds – by working the ground, the seedling is exposed to the sun and dries out
- Hand weeding or mulching is sometimes used on high value crops
- Choice of varieties helps with control as some varieties are better at competing with weeds.

DID YOU KNOW?

Non-organic farmers can use over 450 pesticides. Organic farmers only use pesticides as a last resort. Under Soil Association standards there are only six types of pesticide permitted – and one of those is currently under review. The Soil Association is always looking at ways to improve its standards.

MAKE A SCARECROW

Scarecrows traditionally scare away birds, which can be a pest to a farmer because they eat seeds and crops. Make the frame of a scarecrow out of two lengths of wood forming a cross. Fill an old pillowcase or bag with straw to make a head and then dress the scarecrow with old clothes. See who can design the most stylish or outrageous scarecrow!

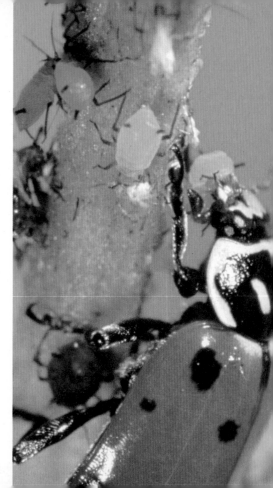

Pest control

Organic farmers believe that healthy plants tend to be more resistant to insect attack. As organic plants grow more slowly, they also have thicker cell walls providing a greater natural barrier to pests. The use of rotations and the choice of hardy varieties is effective in controlling the build up of pests. Ground-covering sheets, together with a small number of pest control products can sometimes be used, but their use is very restricted.

Natural predators

A balanced food chain will have a variety of predators that feed on crop pests. Organic farmers encourage birds, bats and beetles by creating suitable habitats for them. Organic farmers avoid chemical pesticides because they kill the food the predators need to survive – in turn, the predators (for example ladybirds, pictured) kill the pests so the organic farmer does not need to rely on pesticides.

MAKE FRIENDS WITH MINI-BEASTS

See what little creatures or mini-beasts you can find living on the farm:

- Look under stones and dead wood
- Shake branches to see what falls off onto a piece of white paper
- Dig some 'pitfall' traps using yoghurt pots
- Look carefully on plants or on the ground.

Do different creatures prefer different habitats?

Livestock

ANIMAL FARM

Animals look different to humans, but share many common features with us.

As a group, sit in a circle. Each member of the group pretends to be a farm animal.

Then ask each other: 'Do you have fur/two toes/four legs/a tail/etc.' If the answer is 'yes', then the person has to run round the circle and back to their place again.

When you have lots in common (for example two eyes) everyone will get up and run round.

Healthy animals

Organic standards put animal welfare first. Unlike the term 'free-range', organic standards are laid down in law so they guarantee that animals are well treated. Organic farm animals:

- Must have access to fields (when conditions permit) and are truly free range
- Must have plenty of space which helps to reduce stress and disease
- Must be fed a diet free of genetically modified organisms (GMOs)
- Must only be given medicine when the situation demands and not routinely.

Organic livestock farming aims to prevent disease in the first place by promoting health – a healthy animal is better able to resist disease. This is achieved through appropriate diet, high welfare standards for housing and stocking levels, and reducing stress.

WHAT DOES IT MEAN?

Genetically modified/ genetic modification/GM – the insertion of a gene from an animal or plant into the genetic material of another animal or plant. Genetically modified organisms are banned under organic standards. There are concerns about the unknown and long-term effects of GM on our health and the environment.

DID YOU KNOW?

Organic animals must be fed as natural a diet as possible. For example, cattle naturally eat grass, but under non-organic systems they can be fed largely on grain which is not as good for their digestion.

Friesian/Holstein cow

Ayrshire cow

Guernsey cow

Cattle

Cattle breeds have developed over centuries from wild cattle that used to roam Asia and Europe. Humans have bred these domesticated cattle selectively for beef production, dairying or 'dual purpose' (milk and meat).

Cattle are ruminants: they have a stomach of four parts which allows the digestion of cellulose in grass and forage. Because only a little chewing is done before the food is swallowed to the rumen, cows spend considerable time regurgitating and rechewing it. This is called ruminating or 'chewing the cud'.

Dairy cattle

A typical dairy cow has a thin, wedge-shaped body with little flesh and prominent bones. Black and white Friesian/Holstein cows are a common dairy breed, but many organic farms have native Ayrshire, Channel Island or dairy shorthorn breeds. Having been reared in the same region for centuries, these native breeds are well suited to the climate, vegetation and soil. They do well on a grass-based diet – and do not need as much concentrated feed to thrive.

DID YOU KNOW?

No case of BSE has ever been found in an organically born and reared dairy cow. The Soil Association banned animal protein in organic cattle feed as early as 1983.

Why do farmers get up early to milk? Because cows need to be milked at regular intervals – preferably every 12 hours.

Organic milk is stored separately in its own special tanker so it does not mix with non-organic milk.

WHAT DOES IT MEAN?

Ruminant – an animal
that chews the cud.
Rumen – the first stomach
of a ruminant.
Cellulose – chief component
of cell walls of plants and
wood.

DID YOU KNOW?

Store cattle are weaned calves
between one and two years
old. A traditional farming
practice is where store cattle
from the upland districts of the
west and north are fattened on
lowlands elsewhere in the
country. Organic stores are fed
mainly on grass. Barley-beef
type enterprises, where beef
are kept indoors and fattened
intensively on barley or corn,
are prohibited under organic
standards.

The cow produces milk after giving birth to a calf. Organic cows are usually milked no more than twice a day. Cows fed on concentrated feed may produce more milk but it can be stressful for a cow to produce so much milk. Therefore organic cows are fed a grass-based diet, producing a slightly lower but more natural yield.

Beef cattle

A typical beef animal is reared to be eaten – it has a solid, rounded body, well covered in flesh. A range of breeds are commonly used by organic farms. Native breeds are suited to particular parts of the country, for example Highland cattle in Scotland (pictured). It is important to preserve rare breeds as some are in danger of being lost forever.

Suckler herds

Organic farms tend to rear their beef cattle as suckler herds. This is where a cow suckles its calf until it is weaned at about nine months of age, then fattened as store cattle. The cattle are usually kept in family groups to follow their natural herding instincts and reduce stress.

NAME THE BEEF CATTLE

Aberdeen Angus bull

Hereford bull

Welsh black bull

COUNTING SHEEP

The farmer often needs to work out the average number of lambs born to each ewe. This 'lambing average' shows how the flock is performing.

If you visit a farm soon after lambing, you too can work out the average. Look for 10 ewes and then count the number of lambs in their group.

For example if the total number of lambs born to 10 ewes is 15 then the lambing average is 1.5.

Sheep

Sheep have been reared for thousands of years for their meat and wool. The white-faced breeds of sheep seen in Britain today are thought to be descendants of those brought over by the Romans. Many country towns in the UK became rich on the proceeds of wool in medieval times but today, due to the increase in cotton and synthetic fabrics, the emphasis has changed from the sale of wool to the sale of meat.

Upland sheep

Sheep breeds are broadly divided into upland and lowland breeds. Upland breeds are extremely hardy, defying snow and gales and grazing on the meagre grasses. Mountain sheep are territorial and get to know their own part of the mountain: the term for this is 'hefting'. Upland lambs will usually be fattened in the lowlands unless the hill farm has adequate pasture. Although the carcass is small, mountain lamb is renowned for its flavour and texture.

WHAT DOES IT MEAN?

Ewe – female sheep.
Ram – male sheep.
Clean grazing – pasture
that has not been grazed by
the same species of livestock
that season.

DID YOU KNOW?

A sheep has two teats on its
udder whilst a cow has four.
However, a ewe often has up
to three lambs, whilst a cow
usually has only one calf!

Lowland sheep

Most lowland ewes are crossbreds that are reared in upland areas. The lowland ewes are mated with a downland ram to produce lambs that will grow fast. If fed well (or flushed) prior to mating, a lowland ewe will produce mainly twins. Lambing takes place in the spring, usually during March and April.

Organic sheep

Ideally, an organic flock grazes in a rotation with cattle. Rotational grazing means that the farmer will move the sheep on to 'clean grazing' to help prevent the build up of internal parasites and disease, especially important after lambing. An old saying says that sheep should be moved to clean grazing before the church bells ring twice – or before two weeks have elapsed.

To limit the spread of disease, organic standards do not allow the purchase of sheep from livestock markets. Most organic farms will aim to breed their own replacements and therefore have a 'closed flock'.

NAME THE SHEEP

Mountain – Welsh mountain

Upland – Masham

Lowland – Suffolk

NAME THE PIG

Gloucester old spot

Saddleback

Tamworth

Pigs

The pigs of ancient Britain lived mainly in woodlands and provided meat for the Romans, Saxons and Normans. By Tudor times, a large number of pigs were being kept in sties and turned out into woods to forage.

Selective breeding created breeds such as the large white in the 18th century, and Chinese pigs were imported for their meatier carcasses. The second half of the 20th century saw the introduction of intensive pig farming where pigs were kept indoors, often in cramped and restrictive conditions.

Organic pigs

Organic pigs are kept in conditions that, as far as possible, allow them to express their natural behaviour. This includes being kept in family groups with free range access to fields in the grazing season. Strawed winter housing is permitted in severe weather conditions.

Pigs fit into an organic rotation well and add fertility at the end of a grass ley. To prevent the build up of parasites pigs will not graze on the same ground again until four years have elapsed.

DID YOU KNOW?

Animal welfare in organic pig production is paramount and certain practices are prohibited. These include nose ringing and use of farrowing crates (when the sow giving birth is kept in a crate which restricts her movement – and her maternal instincts).

As herbicides are not permitted, pigs can be very effective at controlling persistent weeds through their foraging and rooting.

Native breeds

Native breeds of sow (such as the saddleback) are generally more suited to the extensive organic production system. However, many farmers use a leaner boar, such as the Duroc to reduce fat in the finished carcass. Sows will often have a litter of around 10 piglets and can have two litters a year. Other familiar breeds include the Tamworth (which resembles the ancestral wild pig), Oxford and sandy black (pictured) and the Gloucester old spot.

MAKE AN APPLE PIG

The Gloucester old spot pig used to be known as the 'orchard pig' as it used to graze on windfall apples in the Severn valley. You can make an apple pig with a large apple, a small apple and five cocktail sticks.

- Take the large apple and place it on its side so that the stalk forms the pigs tail and insert four sticks underneath as legs
- Cut the small apple in half and use another stick to attach it to the front of the pig's body. The cut side of the apple is the pig's face and the pips form its nostrils
- You can use other pips for its eyes and leaves for its ears. If you dip the face in vinegar or lemon, it will prevent it from turning brown.

NAME THE POULTRY

Rhode
Island red

Black rock

Bronze turkey

Poultry

Poultry are farm birds and include chicken,
turkeys, ducks and geese.

Chicken

Chicken are believed to have descended from
the jungle fowl in the Asian tropical forests.
Domestic chicken were kept in China up to
4000 years ago but reached Britain at around
AD100. Chicken can be divided into laying or
table birds:

• Laying birds are kept for egg production and
  lay mostly in the spring and summer. Breeds
  include Rhode Island red, black rock (pictured)
  and Columbian blacktail.
• Table birds are kept for meat production
  and are larger and meatier than the layers.
  Current commercial birds are hybrids based
  on traditional breeds such as the Sussex and
  Rhode Island red.

DID YOU KNOW?

Industrial-type battery farms
may keep hens in a cage
where the floorspace is
roughly equivalent to a
sheet of A4 paper. This is
not allowed under organic
standards.

Turkeys

Turkeys are descended from the North American wild turkey which favours a forest habitat. They are usually raised for the Christmas market and many organic farms will rear a flock during the second half of the year.

Organic poultry

Unlike battery farms Soil Association organic poultry are truly free range:

- Flock sizes are limited to 500 per chicken house and the birds are kept in conditions that allow them to express their natural behaviour
- Hens have continuous access to organic land covered with vegetation and are rotated regularly to prevent the build up of disease
- Breeds are selected to be hardy, disease resistant, and docile
- Free range birds need protection from predators. Electric fences are often used to keep out foxes and trees or covered shelters provide additional shade and security
- The Soil Association's organic standards insist on high animal welfare and practices such as routine beak clipping are prohibited.

CHICKEN RUN

Animals need food, water, shelter and space to move – just like human beings.

Rope off a pen about two metres by two metres. Pretend that you are chickens in the pen. It is a little bit squashed and you can think about why it isn't very nice (can't scratch, can't flap your wings and can't run). You are then let out to run around and to become free range organic chickens. If you were a farm animal, how would you prefer to live?

Crops

FLOWER POWER

Mark a small area with a hoop or pegs and string. Look at the number of colours in the area and count the different species of wildflower and grasses. Can you identify any of them?

DID YOU KNOW?

For every hectare, red clover adds as much nitrogen as 200kg of artificial fertiliser.

Grassland

Grass fields are used for grazing livestock. Organic farmers plant clover with the grass to build soil fertility, instead of using artificial fertilisers. Cut grass is used for making silage or hay for winter feed.

Permanent pasture

These are meadows that are never ploughed and therefore tend to have a greater variety of grasses and flowers. Historically they may have survived due to being difficult to work with machinery. Hay made from these pastures tends to be much 'sweeter' due to the variety of grasses, herbs, clovers and plants in the sward.

Leys

Grass/clover leys are grown for perhaps two to four years and will form the basis for animal grazing and winter feed. A typical mixed organic farm will have between 30 and 50 per cent of the area dedicated to grass/clover leys at any particular time.

DID YOU KNOW?

Many once common flowering plants are vanishing from the countryside, victims of chemicals, habitat destruction and over-cropping. As the food for birds and invertebrates, their loss affects the whole food chain.

A study comparing organic and non-organic farms found five times more wild plants and 1.5 times as many species of wild plants on organic farms.

WHAT DOES IT MEAN?

Hay – sun dried grass.
Straw – stalks from cereal.
Nitrogen – essential to life, forming about 78 per cent of the air we breathe, and vital for plant growth. Factory produced nitrogen is applied as a fertiliser by non-organic farmers but this can cause environmental damage. The manufacturing process not only uses a lot of oil but also artificial nitrogen is easily washed away causing pollution in rivers and streams. Organic farmers use clover to add nitrogen to the soil.
Silage – pickled, or fermented, grass.
Sward – carpet of grasses and clovers covering the ground.

Clover

. . . .

Organic farmers grow clover because of its amazing ability to draw nitrogen from the atmosphere into the soil (bacteria living in the root nodules 'fix' the nitrogen, using energy supplied by the plant).

Hay

. . . .

Haymaking is the traditional method of producing winter feed for livestock. The grass is usually cut in summer and allowed to dry in the field. It is turned regularly to help it dry and then baled ready for storage in a barn.

Silage

. . . .

Today, most grass for winter use is made into silage. The grass is cut and wilted in rows (see picture) before being collected by a forage harvester. It is then packed tightly in a plastic-lined silage clamp to remove the oxygen. This airtight store preserves the grass for winter feed, 'pickled' in its own juices. Many farms use big-bale silage wrapped in plastic and stacked on the farm.

NAME THAT GRASS

. . . .

Red clover

Timothy

Cocksfoot

White clover

Ryegrass

NAME THAT FORAGE CROP

Beans

Peas

Stubble turnips

Forage crops

Although grass/clover leys will provide the majority of animal feed required, short-term forage crops can feed livestock early or late in the season. Forage is consumed in its green state, particularly by cattle and horses. When a forage crop is grown between two main crops in a rotation, it is called a 'catch crop'. Forage crops can be split between root crops and leafy crops:

• Root crops include fodder beet, mangels, stubble turnips and swedes. Fodder beet and mangels tend to be harvested from the field and stored in special 'clamps' before feeding to stock
• Leafy forage includes kale, and rape. Some cereals are also grown for forage, notably rye. Leafy forage is usually grazed in the field with an electric strip fence to avoid waste.

Pulses

Peas and field beans are the most common pulses grown in the UK. They both provide a useful break crop between cereals. Like clover, they are legumes and so have the added benefit of fixing nitrogen in the soil.

Field beans

The field bean is usually grown for livestock feed. Deep rooting, it helps improve the soil structure and can add a large amount of organic matter to the soil.

Field peas

These are also grown mainly for livestock feed, either in grain form or as silage. Field peas can also be grown as a green manure or sold fresh to eat. They require a long gap of six or seven years before they are planted on the same land again to prevent the build up of pests and diseases.

WHAT DOES IT MEAN?

Clamp – traditional form of storage in which root vegetables are neatly piled and covered with straw and earth.

Catch crop – cheaper to grow than clover, this extra crop is grown between crops to hold soil together and build fertility (nutrients stored in its leaves are ploughed back into the soil)

Break crop – a change of crop in a rotation. A break crop (like field beans) may be planted between two cereal crops (like wheat and oats). This helps disrupt weeds, pest and disease cycles that could otherwise harm the cereal crop.

Wheat

Barley

Oats

Cereals

Winter cereals are sown in the autumn and spring cereals are sown in the spring. Growing crops in both winter and spring helps by:

- Providing habitats for wildlife (because some creatures need old stubble over winter and others like fresh shoots in spring)
- Allowing the farmer to vary their rotation
- Controlling various pests, weeds and diseases (by breaking up their life cycles).

Harvest time is between July and October and depends on the crop, weather and location. Hot dry weather is needed during harvest because moist grain will spoil in storage. In a wet summer grain can be dried but this is costly and wasteful of energy.

Organic cereals, fertilised by clover leys, take up nutrients slowly. Their cell walls are thicker, making the crop more resistant to pests and diseases. Tall-strawed varieties help shade out and restrict weeds; remaining weeds provide useful habitats for predators such as ladybirds that feed on crop pests.

DID YOU KNOW?

Cereals are a grass species. They start life as green plants (pictured) and only turn the distinctive yellow colour when they ripen in the summer.

WHAT DOES IT MEAN?

Malting – barley is soaked in water and allowed to partly germinate, then dried. The roots and shoots are removed and the remaining grain (malt) is then steeped in water. This solution is used in brewing, while the residual grain is used for animal feed.

Spelt – ancient wheat variety which has less gluten and so can be tolerated by people with a wheat allergy.

Wheat

In Britain, wheat has been grown since before 2000BC, on the higher land above the marshes of the south-west. It is suited to heavy clay soil and most is grown in the east of the country where there is more sun and less rain. Wheat is nutrient-demanding so it will be the first crop that follows grass and clover in the rotation. It is used for a range of products including bread making, biscuits, whiskey and animal feed.

Barley

The ancient Greeks believed that barley was a gift from the god Ceres. Barley was probably first grown in Britain during the Iron Age, on the chalk uplands. Barley has distinctive whiskers or 'awns' on its seed head. As it ripens, the ear bends over until the awns face the ground. Organic farmers usually grow barley for animal feed but it is also used for malting.

Oats

In Europe, wild oats have been grown since before 1000BC with cultivated varieties arriving later. Oats can be grown on a wide range of soils and are suited to the cooler and wetter west and north of the country. Oats are grown for animal feed and human consumption, especially for porridge oats and muesli.

Rye

Rye was new to the Romans, so is not as ancient as oats. It was very popular in the 17th century when rye bread was eaten by about one-seventh of the population. Rye is suited to dry areas where other cereals will not thrive. It is fast growing and provides a good crop for spring grazing by sheep and cattle. Rye bread is still made and the flour is often used as a filler in sauces and soups.

Triticale

Triticale is a cross between wheat and rye. It grows tall (up to two metres) which is good for weed control. Triticale is used for animal feed.

WHAT IS IT MADE OF?

Match the following to the cereal they're made from.

Beer

Bread

Porridge

Beer = Barley Bread = Wheat Porridge = Oats

FRUIT OR ROOT?

Different parts of plants provide us with food. Parts such as the **stem**, **root**, **leaf**, **flower**, **fruit** and **seed**.

Can you match the food below to their correct parts?

Cabbage

Cauliflower

Carrot

Oats

Pear

Rhubarb

Cabbage = Leaf Cauliflower = Flower
Carrot = Root Oats = Seed
Pear = Fruit Rhubarb = Stem

Horticulture

The growing of vegetable crops is called 'horticulture' and it is often seen as separate to farming or 'agriculture'. Horticultural crops can be grown on a field scale, or on smaller beds within a walled garden, greenhouse or polytunnel.

The same principles of crop rotation, weed and pest control apply. Organic standards specify that where crops of the same family are grown in the same soil, there should be an appropriate time lapse between plantings. Additionally, the rotation should include a legume to supply nitrogen for following crops. An example six year horticultural rotation could be clover; followed by potatoes; then legumes; brassicas; roots; and finally salads.

A balanced or self-sustaining rotation can be difficult on small horticultural units due to the need to maximise income from a small area. Therefore, leguminous green manures (such as clover) can be grown as catch crops at frequent intervals throughout the rotation.

WHAT DOES IT MEAN?

Green manure – when ploughed back into the land, it feeds the soil (used instead of compost or manure).

DID YOU KNOW?

A vegetable box scheme can supply a range of seasonal vegetables to your door once a week. Buying this way ensures you get fresh organic vegetables direct from the farm.

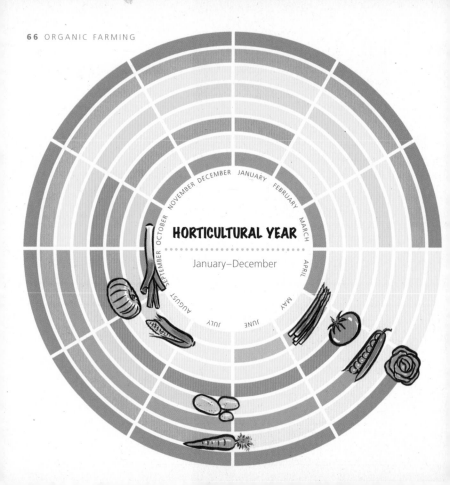

HORTICULTURAL YEAR

January–December

Field scale vegetables

. . . .

Potatoes are the main organic root crop grown in the UK, although organic sugar beet is now the main crop in the eastern counties. Staple vegetables such as carrots, cabbages and cauliflowers are also grown on a field scale.

Both potatoes and carrots are generally grown on ridges to improve soil conditions, weed control and harvesting. Ridges prevent waterlogging and improve drainage.

Walled gardens

. . . .

Walled gardens were built to provide a protective environment for vegetables and fruit. The walls help keep rabbits, livestock and people out, providing a sheltered microclimate with space to suit a wide range of plants.

Today many walled gardens are being brought back to full production by organic growers. They provide an ideal location for small-scale organic horticulture. Polytunnels and greenhouses help to extend the season.

HORTICULTURAL YEAR

. . . .

Cabbages
May–March

Peas
May–September

Tomatoes
May–October

Asparagus
May–June

Carrots
July–March

Potatoes
July–March

Sweetcorn
August–October

Pumpkins
September–January

Leeks
September–April

DID YOU KNOW?

A single greenhouse could grow tomatoes one year, cucumbers the next, followed by peppers and finally salads. Ideally the crops can be rotated around a number of equal sized greenhouses or a number of permanent beds where there is only one greenhouse.

Glasshouse crops

Greenhouses and polytunnels have the benefit of extending the growing season, widening the variety of crops grown, and providing some protection against pests and diseases.

Rotations are more difficult as the traditional crops all come from a small number of plant families. However a break crop such as a green manure, possibly combined with livestock such as poultry, will extend the rotation and reduce the incidence of soil fungi and insect pests such as slugs and snails.

Vineyards

The Romans introduced the vine to the UK and vineyards were thriving by Tudor times. However, the number declined and commercial vineyards had ceased production by 1914. Over the last 30 years a revival has begun and UK organic wine is now available.

DID YOU KNOW?

Vineyards have to go through a three year conversion process before the first organic grapes are harvested. Legumes are planted between the avenues of vines to provide fertility. Mildew diseases can be a problem and are kept at bay by allowing a good flow of air around the vine shoots.

The grapes are picked about the end of October and are immediately crushed and pressed. The fresh juice ferments until Christmas and then matures until bottling in March. The wines are at their best when they have spent between one and two years in the bottle.

Top fruit and orchards

....

Apples, pears, plums and cherries are called top fruit and are usually grown in orchards. Orchards used to be a common feature in the countryside, especially in counties such as Devon, Somerset and Herefordshire. These traditional orchards have declined dramatically since World War II. Devon alone has lost 90 per cent of its traditional orchards and a huge number of local and distinctive varieties of fruit have disappeared.

Organic fruit is now widely available although much of the produce is imported. Orchards require a three year conversion period before the fruit can be sold as organic. Traditional, widely spaced orchard trees are often suited to organic production, especially where a mixture of different varieties help to minimise the impact of pests and disease.

NAME THAT APPLE

....

There are over 2,300 apple varieties in the UK – but today only a few are available in the shops.

Tom Putt

Worcester pearmain

Golden noble

Nature

LEAF RUBBING

Take a piece of paper and crayon and make a rubbing of leaves to compare the different shapes.

Woodland

Ten thousand years ago, after the last ice age, birch, alder, willow and pine trees colonised Britain, to be joined, as the climate improved, by oak, elm and lime. Thus the forest – that five thousand years ago covered 95 per cent of the country – was created. During medieval times these woodlands provided timber as well as a huge range of non-timber products, from forest fruits to fuel to grazing for livestock. Terms such as 'pannage' relate to the ancient right to graze pigs in woodland to forage for acorns and beechmast.

Over the centuries there has been a steady decline in woodland to just five per cent of the UK's land area at the start of the 20th century. Woods are not only cut to make way for roads and cities but also farmland: every field you walk through used to be forest. The woods which remain are often because the soil was unsuitable for farming.

HOW OLD IS THE FOREST?

As they take a very long time to establish themselves, the following springtime flowers are good indicators of an ancient woodland.

Bluebell

Ramsons (wild garlic)

Wood anemone

GOOD WOOD

Look out for the FSC symbols on woodland products in the shops. This proves they come from a sustainable source.

Woodland management

Growing concern for the environment and the need for more home-grown timber has resulted in a new interest in the management of woodland. As a result the total area of forest cover is on the increase.

Demand is growing for timber from sustainable sources and Forest Stewardship Council (FSC) and organic woodland standards help to ensure a high environmental criteria.

Management of woodlands usually includes regular thinning. Removing trees helps provide space and light for the remainder to mature and thrive – without competing for sunlight and nutrients. The early thinnings are for low-value pulp or fire wood, but as the trees mature they become more valuable planking or veneer timber.

Organic standards promote selective felling of trees because a mix of age and species is good for wildlife. Clear felling, an intensive practice which fells all trees in one plot, is more damaging to the landscape. Organic standards also encourage trees grown from seed rather than transplanting trees from another place.

NAME THAT LEAF

Oak

Ash

Beech

Field maple

Scots pine

WHAT DOES IT MEAN?

Wood pasture – either
woodland that has been
grazed for many years, thus
creating a field with trees, or
fields that have been grazed
lightly, allowing new trees
to grow.

Forests and creatures

Livestock can cause a great deal of damage to woodland. However the action of foraging and treading helps disturb the ground which allows a variety of plants to grow – so light grazing can be helpful and encourages natural regeneration.

Wood pasture and parkland

Wood pastures and parkland are the result of centuries of grazing. These habitats are of particular value for the creatures and fungi that live on veteran trees and decaying timber.

Parkland is grassland dotted with mature trees, usually planted by large estates during the 17th and 18th centuries.

Trees in fields

Trees in fields can provide welcome shade for livestock and an attractive landscape feature. Organic standards prohibit the ploughing of land below the canopy of field trees as this can damage the root system and kill the tree.

MEET A TREE

Find an area containing a number of trees and split up into pairs. One of the pair either shuts their eyes or wears a blindfold. The other has to lead the blindfolded one to a tree and ask them to get to know it through touch and smell (feeling the texture of its bark, the size of its trunk, smell of the wood). Then they are led away, the blindfold is taken off – and they have to find it again!

Coppice wood

In a coppice wood, the whole wood was traditionally divided into small areas called 'coupes'. Each year a different coupe was cut or 'coppiced'. This allowed the cut area to regrow before it was cut again. Coppicing can be traced back 6,000 years and was the most widespread woodland activity until the mid 1800s.

Coppicing declined due to reduced demand for coppice products. For example, coke and coal replaced charcoal and firewood for fuel and less hazel was needed for sheep 'hurdles' or fences.

The coppicing process

Some trees do not grow when cut but coppice species are ones that do: they respond to cutting by sending up many stems from the cut stumps or 'stools'. The cutting cycle or rotation varies from seven years for hazel to 25 years for sweet chestnut. This periodic cutting process actually extends the life of most underwood trees and some stools may be several hundred years old.

WHAT DOES IT MEAN?

Underwood – trees like hazel which are shrub sized and form a lower canopy below the taller trees.

Pollarding – traditional method of harvesting timber from certain types of tree. Like coppicing, the new growth is cut regularly in perhaps a 25 year cycle. Unlike coppicng, this is done around two to three metres off the ground so that the new shoots are out of reach of livestock.

Layering – coppice woodland can be renewed by 'layering'. This involves cutting partly through the shoot, bending it down to ground level (pictured) and burying the end in the soil. New life will grow from that point.

NAME THAT CREATURE

Water boatman

Great diving beetle

Pond snail

Water features

Many farms will have water features, from rivers and ponds to saltmarsh and coastline. We all depend on water and care must be taken to avoid depleting this essential resource through contamination. Farm waste and run-off can cause serious pollution, especially through pesticides, nitrates and manures being washed into watercourses.

Organic farms seek to minimise pollution by severely restricting the use of artificial fertilisers. Composting also helps by making farm manures more stable and less likely to leach into watercourses. Wetland areas can also be very important and organic standards prohibit the drainage and over-stocking of these habitats.

Rivers and streams

Every river has its own distinct character and follows a course through a series of habitats, sometimes changing from a fast mountain stream through to a wide estuary where it meets the sea.

DID YOU KNOW?

That you can farm fish? There are organic standards for fish farming (aquaculture). These aim to produce quality fish whilst protecting the welfare of the fish and the environment.

WHAT DOES IT MEAN?

Run-off – rain washes things applied to the land into streams, rivers and ponds.

Wetlands – wet areas of land such as marshes, bogs, or undrained fields.

Saltmarsh – often found on the coast and frequently flooded by sea water. The plants and animals which live here are adapted to these conditions.

The banks and margins of rivers and streams are important for wildlife. Organic standards require adequate borders so that crops are not planted too close to the river bank. This prevents erosion and soil run-off. Willow and alder trees favour wet conditions and historically many of these were 'pollarded' to provide firewood or withies for basket making.

Ponds

Ponds have clearly defined margins and are one of the easiest habitats to observe and understand. They are crammed with plants and animals, from masses of microscopic algae to roaming carnivorous fish. Some farm ponds were historically created for livestock to drink from, for example 'dew ponds'. You may also see new lakes or reservoirs on farms that are used for irrigating crops, especially for horticulture.

WHAT'S IN THE POND?

What creatures are living in the pond, stream – or even a water trough? You need a pond dipping net and an empty pot. Slowly sweep the net through the water and empty the contents into the pot. Can you see any of the creatures shown on page 82? Replace them carefully in the water afterwards.

Remember – only go near the water with an adult, even if the water looks shallow.

FOOD CHAIN GAME

Make five cards with one picture on each: barley, aphid, ladybird, skylark and hawk. Get in line to form a food chain (barley next to aphid, next to ladybird, next to skylark, next to hawk).

Someone pretends to be a farmer and sprays chemicals to kill the aphid. The aphid card leaves the line.

Without the aphid, the ladybird has nothing to eat and so leaves the line too. This affects the skylark, and so on, demonstrating that all living things are connected.

Wildlife

Organic farming helps provide habitats for wildlife. Birds, bats and beetles make their homes on the edge of fields (field margins), in hedgerows and trees. On an organic farm, the fields growing crops can also provide homes for wildlife too. This is because of the restricted use of chemicals, allowing more wildlife to survive.

Food chains

Organic farms encourage a balanced 'food chain' to help support the farming system. A food chain starts with the soil which enables plants to grow. These plants in turn feed herbivores (for example insects) which in turn are eaten by carnivores (for example spiders and song birds). All these inter-connections form the 'food web'. A good indicator of a balanced food web will be the number of carnivores (for example birds of prey) in the area. As they are at the 'top' of a food chain, it shows that there is plentiful life 'below' them.

WHAT DOES IT MEAN?

Food chain – who eats who, from the insect which nibbles on a leaf to the bird which eats the insect.

Food web – different food chains are part of a bigger system called the food web – which includes the multiple connections between all parts of life.

DID YOU KNOW?

Studies have found that organic farms have up to five times more wild plants than non-organic farms.

PLANT POINTS

Learn more about the different parts of a plant. Call out the name of a part of the plant (for example 'leaf'). The first person to touch that part wins a point.

Make the game more difficult by calling out different plant types (for example, daisy, wheat or even an oak tree).

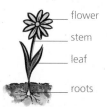

flower

stem

leaf

roots

Invertebrates

Invertebrates are animals without backbones, such as insects, spiders and centipedes. These provide food for many birds and their young. Predatory invertebrates also play a vital role in keeping down pest populations for farmers. For example ladybirds, hoverflies and lacewing larvae are voracious eaters of aphids.

Bees and butterflies provide an important role for the farmer by pollinating crops. Look out for beehives where the beekeeper will harvest honey. Butterflies are best seen on calm sunny days in the summer.

Wild flowers

Although 95 per cent of farmland grows crops, organic methods enable arable flowers to survive in this cropped area, mainly due to the lack of herbicides. These plants in turn provide homes and food for other invertebrates and animals. Organic standards also prohibit the ploughing of species-rich meadows. Over-stocking of animals is also prevented in organic farming – this prevents flowers from being lost through over-grazing.

GET THE BUG

How many legs do different bugs have? Pretend to be your favourite mini-beast. For example, three could join up and pretend to be a bee with six legs, four could be a spider with eight legs or a whole line could pretend to be a millipede.

DID YOU KNOW?

Organic farms have 1.6 times as many invertebrates as non-organic farms and twice as many spiders.

WHAT'S THAT SOUND?

On the farm there is a lot more going on than you might think. Find a quiet spot, close your eyes and listen to what sounds you can hear around you. Put one finger up in the air for each new sound, such as birdsong, rustling leaves and farm machinery. With your eyes still closed, can you point to where the sounds are coming from? There is a lot more going on than you can see!

Birds

. . . .

Farmland birds are a favourite feature of the countryside but numbers have fallen considerably over the last few decades. Skylark numbers fell by 75 per cent on farmland between 1972 and 1996, partridge numbers have fallen by 82 per cent and tree sparrow by 89 per cent – largely attributed to intensive farming.

Organic farms are helping to reverse these trends because they provide food (like invertebrates), crops and habitats for birds. Different bird species prefer different habitats, for example partridges are usually found around the field margins whilst lapwings (pictured) skylarks tend to be found in the middle of the field.

Many bird species are more numerous on organic farms. The total bird population has been shown to be over twice as high, probably due to the avoidance of pesticides (meaning more bird food) and different cropping practices (meaning more homes for birds).

SIGNS OF BIRD LIFE

. . . .

Feathers

Tracks

Nests

DORMOUSE LIVING

Hollowed out nut

Nest

Dormouse

Mammals

••••••••••••••••••••••••••••••••••••••

There are around 60 species of wild mammals found in the UK, including 14 types of bat and 15 types of rodent. Eight of these species have been introduced to the UK within the last 200 years, for example grey squirrel, muntjac deer and mink. These have in many cases thrived whilst some of our native species, such as red squirrels and otters, have declined.

Mammals, like the fallow deer (pictured), tend to be secretive and their presence is usually indicated by their tracks and signs. These are often the best way to find out what wild animals are living on the farm. However, if you are quiet, you may be lucky in seeing some animals, especially around dusk.

ANIMAL TRACKS

•••••••••••••••••••••••

Deer

Badger

Farm visits

In the past, communities were closely linked to farms which grew their food – in the 18th century, 40 per cent of the population worked on the land. Today, the number of people employed by agriculture has dropped to 2.5 per cent.

As a result our understanding of where food comes from and how it is grown has declined.

Organic production is more labour intensive and organic farms employ 30 per cent more labour. This is good for jobs and the rural economy.

Open days and events

Throughout the year, many farms run special open days (such as lambing days, pictured) and farm walks. These provide an excellent opportunity to talk to the farmer and see at first hand what is special about the farm. Many farms will put on special tractor and trailer tours, displays and even stalls of local crafts and produce.

To find out more about these events, contact the Soil Association at the address on the back of this book.

Arranging your visit

Check for opening times. Some farms are open all the time, others are only open to groups by arrangement. Some farmers may charge a small fee for guided tours (to account for their time spent away from their work to show you around).

Ensure you take appropriate footwear and waterproofs to avoid a soaking in wet weather.

THE COUNTRY CODE

Remember to follow the country code. The farm is both home and livelihood for the farmer so please treat it with respect:

- Take your litter home with you
- Leave gates as you find them
- Do not disturb livestock or wildlife
- Keep to marked paths.

Dogs may not be allowed on some farms (to avoid disturbance to wildlife or farm animals). Please check with the farm beforehand.

WHAT DOES IT MEAN?

Food miles – is the term used to indicate the distance between where the food came from and where it is eaten.

WHAT'S FOR LUNCH?

Where does the food you eat come from? Is your food grown in the UK or overseas? A lot of the food we eat can easily be sourced locally, but comes from abroad (for example apples from New Zealand). Can you think of ways to reduce food miles?

Farm shopping

Much of the food produced by organic farms is sold to wholesalers or supermarkets. However farmers are increasingly selling direct to the consumer. Buying your food this way supports the farmer and reduces the environmental cost of transporting food.

DID YOU KNOW?

Organic principles extend beyond the farm gate and encompass the whole food farm system. They aim, where possible, to develop local food economies so that the financial and environmental costs of transporting food are kept to a minimum.

OPEN ALL HOURS

Where can you buy direct from the farm? Does the farm you are visiting have a:

- Vegetable or meat box scheme
- Farm shop (pictured)
- A stall at a farmers' market?

REGULAR VISITS

Many schools develop regular links with one local farmer. If a farm is used every year a good relationship is built up. The same worksheets and maps can be used and both teacher and farmer learn what activities and features of the visits are successful.

School visits

A visit to an organic farm is a valuable way of enriching your students' experience and can be used as a resource to meet targets in almost all areas of the national curriculum. Organic farms are particularly suitable as most will have a mixture of crops and livestock. This diversity makes them rich in features which provide a satisfying and fulfilling experience for pupils and teachers alike.

Farms are usually very exciting and motivating places for children. Careful research and preparation is important to get the most out of what is available. The potential list of topics that can be tackled on the farm is wide, so it is important to be clear about what the visit aims to do and how this relates to other work children are doing on the national curriculum.

DID YOU KNOW?

Many farmers are happy
to visit schools to talk about
their farm. You may like to
invite the farmer along to
your school for the children
to show him or her the work
done after their visit.

SAFETY

As on any other visit, safety considerations should be paramount. The combination of a farm and children pose particular considerations as far as safety is concerned.

Be sure to familiarise yourself with the summary of the Health and Safety Executive's advice (see p106) and get a copy for yourself and other adults on the trip.

Pay particular attention to hand washing and make sure children do so as often as possible, especially after being in touch with farm animals.

Check that the school's insurance covers farm visits and that any requirements on pupil-teacher ratios and supervision can be met.

Some guidance for teachers

To prepare for your visit, first locate your local farm and see whether it is suitable for what you have in mind. It is probably worth speaking with the farmer on the telephone to discuss your requirements.

You should visit the farm ahead of your class visit to look over the farm and discuss the itinerary with the farmer or education officer. This will be an opportunity for you to find out about the farm, and for the farmer to find out about the school and your students.

Following your initial visit, send a letter to the farmer confirming date, arrival time, and the number of children, teachers and parents arriving. You may need to send a purchase order so that the farm can send an invoice if they charge for the visit.

Find out what resources and materials are available and discuss with the farmer what previous groups have done. Check out the Soil Association's website for ideas for you to do both on the farm and in the classroom.

DISCIPLINE

A clear understanding between farmer, teacher and children regarding discipline needs to be established before any visit takes place. You will need to take the lead on this as most farmers will not be experienced at looking after groups of children.

NATIONAL CURRICULUM

Many of the activities in this book provide possible links into many areas of the national curriculum for key stages 1 and 2.

KEY STAGE 1

SCIENCE

Scientific enquiry

Investigative skills (2a–j) planning; obtaining and presenting evidence; consider evidence and evaluation; (2f) explore, using senses:
- Flower power (p54)
- Farm detective (p10)
- Meet a tree (p79)
- What's that sound? (p90)

Life processes and living things

Life processes:
- What's in the pond? (p85)
- Animal farm (p34)

Humans and other animals:
- Animal farm (p34)

Green plants:
- Fruit or root? (p64)
- Plant points (p88)

Variation and classification:
- Animal farm (p34)

Living things in their environment:
- Make friends with mini-beasts (p31)
- Animal farm (p34)
- Flower power (p54)
- What's in the pond? (p85)

Materials and their properties

Grouping materials
- Barn builder (p22)

GEOGRAPHY

Geographical enquiry and skills

(1b) observation and recording; (2e) making maps and plans:
- Natural map (p11)
- Map stick (p8)

(2b) Use fieldwork skills
- Flower power (p54)

Knowledge and understanding of place

(3a) Identify and describe places:
- Natural map (p11)

ART

(1a,b) exploring and developing ideas; (2a–c) investigating and making
- Make a scarecrow (p30)
- Leaf rubbing (p74)

PSHE/CITIZENSHIP

(1) developing confidence
and responsibility;
(2) preparing to play an
active role as citizens
• Chicken run (p51)
• What's for lunch? (p98)

KEY STAGE 2

SCIENCE

Scientific enquiry

Investigative skills; (2a–m)
planning; obtaining and
presenting evidence;
consider evidence
and evaluation:
• Flower power (p54)

Life processes and living things

Life processes:
• What's in the pond? (p85)
• Flower power (p54)

Humans and other animals:
• Animal farm (p34)

Green plants:
• Fruit or root? (p64)
• Flower power (p54)

Variation and classification:
• What's in the pond? (p85)

Living things in their
environment:
• Make friends with
mini-beasts (p31)
• Animal farm (p34)
• Flower power (p54)
• What's in the pond? (p85)
• Food chain game (p86)

Materials and their properties

Grouping and classifying
materials:
• Barn builder (p22)

GEOGRAPHY

Geographical enquiry and skills

(1b) observation and
recording; (2e) making maps
and plans:
• Natural map (p11)
• Map stick (p8)

(2b) Use fieldwork skills:
• Flower power (p54)
• What's in the pond? (p85)

Knowledge and understanding of place

(3a) identify and describe
places; (3g) recognise how
places are interdependent:
• Natural map (p11)
• What's for lunch? (p98)

Knowledge and understanding of patterns and processes

Knowledge and Understanding of environmental change & sustainable development
• What's for lunch? (p98)

PSHE/CITIZENSHIP

Developing confidence and responsibility; (1a) talk and write about their opinions and explain their views:
• Chicken run (p51)
• What's for lunch? (p98)

(2) Preparing to play an active role as citizens
• Chicken run (p51)
• What's for lunch? (p98)

(3) Developing a healthy, safer lifestyle
• Chicken run (p51)
• What's for lunch? (p98)

MATHEMATICS

Calculations

Mental methods involving the number operations:
• How old is that hedge? (p18)
• Counting sheep (p40)

Solving numerical problems

Real life situations using the number operations:
• Counting sheep (p40)

HEALTH & SAFETY GUIDANCE

While the hazard from infection resulting from a farm visit is real, the risks are readily controlled by everyday measures. The following sensible steps will help make your visit even more safe, healthy and enjoyable.

BEFORE YOUR VISIT

• Discuss visit arrangements with the farmer
• Read and understand the advice in the main AIS23 information sheet (see 'further information')
• Decide what ratio of adults:pupils. As a general rule, 1:4 for 3–5 year olds, and 1:8 for 5–8 year olds
• Ensure supervisors understand the need to follow the rules

- Discuss with pupils the rules for the visit
- Make sure that pupils wear appropriate clothing and footwear, and that cuts or grazes are covered with a waterproof dressing.

DURING AND AFTER YOUR VISIT

Make sure that the children:
- Do not kiss animals, suck fingers or put pencils in mouths
- Wash hands thoroughly before and after eating, after any contact with animals and again before leaving the farm
- Never eat food which has fallen to the ground, or taste animal foods
- Clean boots thoroughly before leaving

- Check that the children stay in their allocated groups during the visit
- Do not use or pick up tools, climb on to walls or animal pens
- Listen carefully and follow the instructions and information given by the farm staff
- Approach and handle animals quietly and gently.

REMEMBER

The children are your responsibility and should be supervised during the visit, especially during hand washing. If a member of your group shows signs of illness after a visit, advise their parent/guardian to visit the doctor and explain that they have had recent contact with animals.

FURTHER INFORMATION

Information sheet and supplement (AIS23) are available free from:
HSE Books, PO Box 1999, Sudbury, Suffolk CO10 2WA.
T 01787 881165
F 01787 313995
www.hsebooks.co.uk

Soil Association

The Soil Association is an independent not-for-profit membership organisation and one of the UK's most respected environmental groups.

For the past 50 years the organisation has grown in complexity and scope but, at heart, its mission remains the same, to promote the relationship between a sustainable system of agriculture and human and environmental health.

The Soil Association's wholly-owned subsidiary, Soil Association Certification Ltd, is the largest of the UK organic certification bodies and currently certifies over 70 per cent of UK licensed producers and processors. Its nine independent standards committees continue to develop and maintain standards, both nationally and internationally, at the very highest levels under a symbol that people can trust.

Principal services include: building consumer awareness, market and supply chain development, producer and processor support, standard setting, policy development and campaigning for policy change and best practice throughout the whole food chain.

DID YOU KNOW?

The Soil Association is a charity that relies on the support of individual members of the general public to continue its work.

If you want organic food and a living countryside – please join us today.

BENEFITS OF JOINING

Free – *The Truth About Food* a 44-page booklet revealing that facts about what you eat, yours with a monthly payment.
Free – to all members, *Living Earth* magazine with thought provoking writing and contributions from writers like Monty Don.

To join or donate please call **0117 914 2447**.

Acknowledgements

Written, researched and produced by the Soil Association.

Illustrations

Simon Roberts (www.sr-illustration.com).

Photography

Geoff Wilkinson/*You*: cover cow, pig and sheep; p3, 7, 33, 37, 42, 45, 65 and 68. Charles Sainsbury-Place/Soil Association: cover field; p9, 25, 35, 53, 55 and 78. Rupert Aker/Soil Association: p19, 21, 23, 38, 49, 75, 83, 88, 97, 99, 101 and 102. Jim Hudson/Soil Association: p41, 56, 70 and 84. Gaia Books: p13, 27 and 28 (from the Gaia 'organic basics' series: *Compost*; *Pests*; *Soil*; *Weeds*). Grantly Lynch: p14 and 95. Paul Carter/Soil Association: p17 and 61. Ian Britton/Freefoto.com: p73 and 92. Soil Association: p10, 26 and 46. Riverford Organic Vegetables Ltd: p5. Martin Peck: p50. Ian Rowland: p81. Edward Parker: p77. Fiona Russell/Soil Association: p87. RSPB images: p90. Jason Ingram/Soil Association: p110.